Acknowledgements

Almost every family has a treasured recipe – the casserole that's always on the menu for Christmas dinner...the money cakes created for birthdays...Aunt Clare's cookies that are requested for every family event...

These recipes are beloved as much for the memories they evoke or the special family member who created them, as they are for how they taste.

Most families have many such recipes, handed down through generations - often made for the children or grandchildren... taught to adults – sometimes through Skype or Email – as a grown-up child wants to start creating his/her own food traditions...or simply squirreled away on index cards or scraps of paper.

It is in discovering these recipes that we are often provided with a glimpse into our family's history – the culinary creativity of difficult financial times...the solutions to family meals when both parents entered/returned to the workforce...the introduction of new or novel processed products into our culture.

Food – what we cook, what we eat, and the individuals with whom we share our daily bread have been proven to have huge social repercussions. It is with this knowledge that we chose to introduce Chase to the Family Cookbook. And that we invite you dear reader, to start the exploration of your own culinary family tree.

FIRST EDITION

Dawn Ius, *writer*
James Grasdal, *illustrator*
Alberta Canola Producers Commission, *publisher*
780.454.0844
Edmonton, Alberta
Canada T5L 4S6
www.canola.ab.ca

Published by the Alberta Canola Producers Commission (ACPC)

www.canola.ab.ca

The ACPC has as its mandate to improve the long-term profitability of Alberta canola producers. This includes the goal: to maintain awareness and develop understanding of the role that canola plays as one of Canada's major agricultural commodities. We believe that an entertaining story that links a local food like canola, the story of cooking and family recipes will help to meet that goal. Thank you to www.canolainfo.org and www.healthyu.com for recipes and inspiration to modify recipes.

ISBN: 978-0-9680149-5-0

First Printing
June 2013

Printed in Canada
By Burke Group of Companies
17407-106 Ave NW
Edmonton, AB T5S 1E7

Tasting My Story

Written by Dawn Ius
Illustrated by James Grasdal

Chase Duffy stared at the new kid standing at the front of the Food Studies class with his hands behind his back. What was up with the white apron and chef's hat?
It wasn't even Halloween.
"Let's welcome Nikolai Driscoll. Just in time for the annual bake-off and sale. Nikolai's father is a famous chef from the area – the rest of you will have your work cut out for you."
Chase rolled his eyes. Well that explained the cheesy costume. Chase dreaded this event – cooking was so boring.
Do we have to participate?

Mr. Lawrence's lips pressed together in a frown.
You know the answer to that, Chase.
All proceeds from the bake sale this year will go to the school library.
Well, that certainly changed things.
Lightening piped up...
What do we win?
Personal satisfaction? For some of you, this could lead to a career in the cooking industry.

Chase doubted that, but he didn't like the smug look stretched across Nikolai's face. His adrenaline spiked.
"My mom's recipe for cinnamon buns is the best."
"They won't hold a candle to my award-winning brownies."
Nothing wrong with a little bit of friendly competition, boys. But let's not get carried away.
Chase grinned. He might not have a famous chef in his back pocket, but he had Grandma. He'd bet she knew a recipe that was out of this world.

Chase burst through the front door of his grandparent's house.
Grandma!
He peered into the kitchen. She wasn't at the sink.
Wasn't at the stove.
Chase glanced at the clock. It was after breakfast – where was she?
He called her name again.

In here...
He followed the voice into his grandparent's bedroom.
Grandma knelt on the floor, her head buried in a wooden trunk that looked like a giant treasure chest.

She looked up.
Chase, what are you doing here so early?
Chase took in the scene, his grandmother's messy hair, her wide eyes and pale skin. Clothes, bed sheets, trinkets and books littered the floor at her feet.
Grandma, what are you looking for?

"Oh dear, I'm just so forgetful.
I've lost the key to this box."
Chase lifted the box off the floor. It was fastened shut by a rusted, antique-looking lock.
He sniffed the box. It didn't smell funny.
He tugged on the lock.
Nothing happened.
What's inside?
"That's not important," Grandma said. Her hands were in the treasure chest again, rummaging around.
"Please, help me find the key."

Chase knelt on the floor for a better look.
Pens
Pins
Boxes
Pictures
Glasses
Magazines
Medals
The scent of his family's history swirled under his nostrils.
ACHOOOOOo
Dust escaped into the air.
Wait...
What was that?
Chase reached into the chest, pulled out a heavy book and wiped away a layer of dust...
Family Recipes

As in his family's recipes?
Just what he needed!
Chase sat down on the floor
and crossed his legs.
He set the book across his lap.
Grandma, what's this?
Family
Recipes
It's a book of magic.
Magic?
Chase groaned.
"Come on Grandma.
Don't kid around.
Really."
What
is
it?
Family
Recipes

That was my great, great, great grandmother Josephine's.
Grandma pulled an old hat out from the treasure chest and set it on her head. Chase bit back a laugh.
"Way back at the turn of the century, Grandma Josephine started a cookbook. Over the years, we've added to it."

There's more than just recipes in there, Chase.
You can learn a lot about my family history by reading all of the notes.
Even from the first recipe, those delicious baking powder biscuits...
Family Recipes
Grandma's voice faded. Chase's fingers tingled. The words seemed to pop off the page. The room spun until...

The grunt and whir of machinery plodding across a vast field of green and brown replaced the silence. The tops of ancient tractors pulled multiple-blade ploughs-so different from the modern equipment Grandpa used on his canola field.
A chicken clucked at Chase's feet.

Startled, he realized he stood in a chicken coop, with dozens of hens and roosters pecking at the dirt. Across the yard, a hen laid a fresh egg while on the other side of the field, a cow mooed. Chase walked around the hen house and stumbled towards the fence where four pigs frolicked in the mud.

The voice travelled from the front porch of a small, rustic farmhouse just on the other side of the pigpen.
A young woman stood waving her hands in the air and ringing a bell, trying to catch the attention of the man driving the tractor.
The old machine came to a stop and the woman went back inside. Chase's stomach began to grumble.
Maybe he could stop in for a bite to eat, figure out where he was – and how to get back to Grandma's.

He knocked on the outside door.
No answer.
Hello? Excuse me...?
Chase pushed the door open and peered inside the small kitchen. The woman pulled a pan of biscuits from the oven, and when she turned around to set them on the counter, Chase thought she looked like a much younger version of his Grandmother.

I'm sorry to bother...
But I think I'm lost.
The woman, whistling an unfamiliar tune, danced around the kitchen as though she hadn't heard him.
The smell of those biscuits made Chase's stomach roar.
So loud he thought for sure the woman would hear it.
GRRRRRRRRRRRRRRRRRR
Except she didn't notice Chase at all. She removed several biscuits from the cookie sheet and set them on two plates.

She walked over to the opposite counter
where a book lay open.
Chase crept closer for a better look.
He recognized the pages right away.
The family cookbook!
And right next to it,
a long, metal skeleton key.
It had to be Grandma's.
He reached over to grab it,
but all he got was a fistful of air.
Josephine, those biscuits smell delicious!

Chase looked over his shoulder
for the source
of the booming voice.
The man was tall
and rugged looking,
almost a giant, really.
And burly, too.
Straw and dirt covered his pants.
He wiped his hand
across his forehead.
"We're going to have a great wheat
crop this year, sweetie."

I'm proud of you, Ernie.
Ernie patted the chair next to him. "Sit and have a biscuit with me." He bit into one and smacked his lips together. "You'd best keep this recipe under lock and key."
Josephine grabbed the old key and slipped it onto the chain around her neck. She turned and winked. Chase swore she was looking right at him.

Pioneer Biscuits

Simple, quick and easy to do.

How Many: 1 for you and 14 friends (15 biscuits)

What You Need:

1 cup barley flour, 250 mL
1 cup whole wheat flour, 250 mL
2 tsp baking powder, 10 mL
½ cup canola oil, 125 mL
⅔ cup milk, skim or 1%, 150 mL

What You Do:

1. Preheat oven to 425°F (220°C). Take out a baking sheet and set aside for now. Clean an area of the counter where you can knead the dough.
2. Measure the barley flour, whole wheat flour and baking powder and place in a medium-sized bowl. Mix together.
3. Make a well in the centre of the dry ingredients. Measure and pour the canola oil and milk into the well.
4. Using a fork, mix until a dough forms and pulls away from the sides of the bowl to form a ball.
5. Sprinkle some flour on the cleaned counter top.
6. Place the dough on the floured surface and knead lightly 10 times. Kneading the dough is done by pulling the sides of the dough further away from you and folding it towards yourself. Fold the dough in half and use your body weight to push the dough into itself. Give the dough a quarter turn. Grab the other side and fold it in half. Again, push the newly folded half into itself. Repeat 10 times.
7. Roll or pat out dough to 3/8 inch (1 cm) thickness.
8. Cut the dough into circles of approximately 1 ½ inches (4 cm) in diameter using a cookie cutter or small glass.
9. Place the circles of dough on an ungreased baking sheet.
10. Bake in preheated oven for 10 to 12 minutes.
11. Serve the biscuits warm with peanut butter or low-fat cream cheese.

How healthy is it?

1 serving (1 biscuit) – Calories 132, Total Fat 7.9 g, Saturated Fat 0.7 g, Cholesterol 1 mg, Sodium 70 mg, Carbohydrates 14 g, Fibre 2 g, Protein 3 g, Potassium 76 mg

Fill, Fold & Fuel Crepes

Fun to fill, roll or fold and eat with your hands.

How Many: 1 for you and 7 friends (8 crepes)

What You Need:

2 eggs
3 Tbsp canola oil, 45 mL
1 cup milk, skim or 1%, 250 mL
¾ cup barley flour, 175 mL
1 Tbsp granulated sugar, 15 mL

What You Do:

1. Cut 8 squares of wax paper.
2. In a small bowl, crack 1 egg. Transfer to a blender or a medium-sized bowl. Make sure there are no shells with your egg. Crack the second egg and add to the first.
3. Measure canola oil and milk, adding to the cracked eggs. Blend on medium speed, or if using a whisk mix the liquid ingredients until well blended.
4. Measure the barley flour and the granulated sugar. Add to the liquid ingredients and continue to blend until mixed well.
5. Heat a non-stick frying pan or crepe pan over medium high heat.
6. Pour about ¼ cup (50 mL) of batter into the pan and tilt the pan in all directions to form a round shape.
7. Cook the crepe for about 1 minute, or until golden brown underneath.
8. Carefully remove the crepe from the pan and lay it on one piece of wax paper
9. Continue making crepes until all the batter is used up.
10. Place a sheet of wax paper between each crepe to prevent the crepes from sticking together.
11. Serve warm with a variety of toppings – Greek yogurt, fruit, frozen yogurt.
12. Crepes can be prepared ahead and refrigerated for up to 2 days. Crepes may also be frozen for up to 1 month, if they are tightly wrapped in foil or plastic.

How healthy is it?

1 serving (1 crepe) – Calories 90, Total Fat 4.8 g, Saturated Fat 0.7 g, Cholesterol 39 mg, Sodium 24 mg, Carbohydrates 9 g, Fibre 1 g, Protein 3 g, Potassium 73 mg

Lemony-Berry Muffins To-Go

Sweet and sour. Yum!

How Many: 1 for you and 23 friends (24 muffins) or breakfast on-the-go for one month if muffins are well wrapped in plastic and frozen.

What You Need:

¾ cup whole wheat flour, 175 mL
¾ cup barley flour, 175 mL
½ cup granulated sugar, 125 mL
2½ tsp baking powder, 12 mL
¾ cup Saskatoon berries, 175 mL
1 egg
¼ cup canola oil, 60 mL
¾ cup milk, skim or 1%, 175 mL

Note: If you do not have Saskatoon berries, you can use other berries such as raspberries, blueberries or strawberries.

Topping:

1 Tbsp lemon rind (outer peel of the lemon), grated, 15 mL
1 Tbsp granulated sugar, 15 mL
¼ cup sliced almonds, 50 mL

What You Do:

1. Preheat oven to 425°F (220°C).
2. Prepare a muffin pan by oiling each of the muffin tins with canola oil.
3. Prepare topping by first washing fresh lemon well.
4. Grate lemon rind – just the outside yellow part of the lemon.
5. Measure lemon rind and place in a small bowl. Add granulated sugar and mix well.
6. Measure and sift flour into a medium-sized bowl.
7. Measure granulated sugar and baking powder and add to the flour. Mix well.
8. Stir in Saskatoon berries.
9. In a separate bowl, crack the egg, making sure to not get any egg shells in with the egg. Measure canola oil and milk, and add to the cracked egg. Mix well.
10. Add the liquid ingredients to the dry ingredients and mix until barely moistened.
11. Spoon batter into muffins tins, filling them three quarters full.
12. Top each muffin with about a pinch of the lemon rind and sugar topping mixture.
13. Add a few almond slices to each muffin.
14. Bake muffins in preheated oven for 8-10 minutes or until nicely browned.

How healthy is it?

1 serving (1 muffin) – Calories 85, Total Fat 3.1 g, Saturated Fat 0.4 g, Cholesterol 11 mg, Sodium 63 mg, Carbohydrates 13 g, Fibre 1 g, Protein 2 g, Potassium 51 mg

Stampede Pancakes

Thousands served every year as part of the Calgary Stampede festivities.

How Many: 1 for you and 6 friends (7 – 5" [25 cm] pancakes)

What You Need:

1⅓ cups barley or whole-wheat flour, 325 mL
1 tsp granulated sugar, 5 mL
1 Tbsp baking powder, 15 mL
1¼ cups milk, skim or 1%, 300 mL
1 egg
1 Tbsp canola oil, 15 mL
½ tsp vanilla, 2.5 mL

What You Do:

1. In medium mixing bowl, measure and mix the flour, sugar and baking powder.
2. Make a well in the center of the dry ingredients.
3. Crack an egg and add it to the well, making sure to not get any egg shell in with the egg.
4. Measure the milk, canola oil and vanilla and add to the well.
5. Mix well.
6. Place non-stick frying pan on the stove. Set the temperature to medium heat.
7. Using a quarter cup measure, spoon batter into non-stick frying pan.
8. When bubbles start to form on top, use a spatula to flip the pancake.
9. When pancake is brown underneath, it is ready to eat or serve.
10. Serve with fruit, yogurt or low-sugar pancake syrup if desired.

How healthy is it?

1 serving (1 pancake) – Calories 79, Total Fat 2.0 g, Saturated Fat 0.4 g, Cholesterol 18 mg, Sodium 128 mg, Carbohydrates 13 g, Fibre 2 g, Protein 3 g, Potassium 82 mg

Peek-a-Boo Breakfast

An all-in-one breakfast!

How Much: Enough for only you

What You Need:

canola-cooking spray
1 slice whole-wheat or 9-grain bread
1 egg,
dash pepper or hot sauce (if you choose)

What You Do:

1. Using a cookie cutter or a water glass, cut a hole (large enough to hold the egg) in the center of the slice of bread.
2. Spray a small non-stick fry pan with canola baking spray.
3. Place the frying pan on the stove set on medium high heat.
4. Put the bread in the pan.
5. Crack open the egg in a small bowl.
6. Carefully pour the egg into the hole in the bread.
7. Reduce heat and cook slowly, until the egg is just cooked through.
8. Season with pepper, if you wish.
9. You may also want to add salsa to your breakfast.
   Enjoy!

How healthy is it?

1 serving– Calories 157, Total Fat 6.7 g, Saturated Fat 2.1 g, Cholesterol 226 mg, Sodium 198 mg, Carbohydrates 12 g, Fibre 2 g, Protein 11 g, Potassium 157 mg

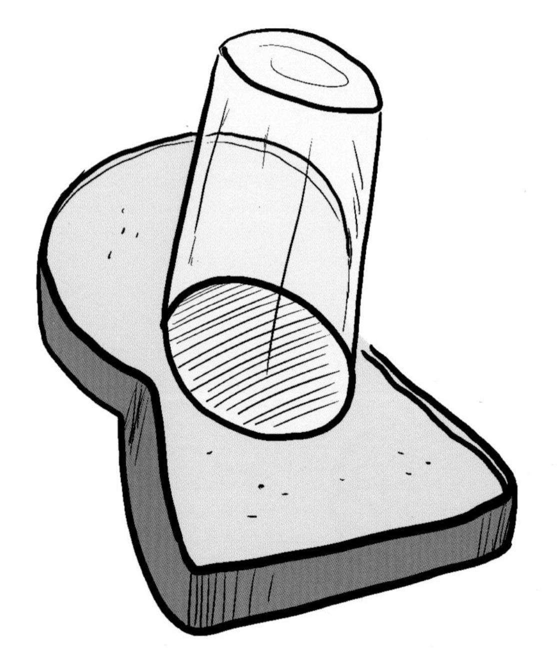

Canola Granola

Good as a snack, or eat with yogurt and fruit in a breakfast parfait.

How much: 1 serving for you and 11 friends (12 – a cup [75 ml] serving)

What you need:

canola oil cooking spray
2 cups rolled oats, 500 mL
⅓ cup ground flaxseed, 75 mL
½ cup (2 oz/55g) almond slices, 125 mL
2 tsp ground cinnamon, 10 mL
¼ cup canola oil, 50 mL
¼ cup honey or maple syrup, 50 mL
1 Tbsp low-fat milk, 15 mL
2 tsp vanilla extract, 10 mL
1 cup dried fruit – apples, raisins, cherries, etc. – 250 mL
1 Tbsp orange zest, optional, 15 mL

What you do:

1. Preheat oven to 300°F (150°C).
2. Coat a baking sheet with canola oil cooking spray.
3. Measure and combine oats, flaxseed, almonds, and cinnamon.
4. In a smaller bowl, measure and combine the canola oil, honey or syrup, milk and vanilla.
5. Pour liquid mixture over the oat mixture, stirring constantly.
6. Spread mixture on a baking sheet in a layer ¼-inch (1 cm) thick.
7. Bake in the warmed oven for 10 minutes.
8. Stir the granola mixture and return to the oven for another 10 minutes.
9. Remove the granola mixture from the oven, stir one final time and cook another 10 minutes or until the mixture is browned, but not burnt.
10. Remove from the oven and sprinkle evenly with dried fruit and orange zest.
11. Cool completely.
12. Store in an airtight container in the refrigerator for up to two weeks.

How healthy is it?

1 serving (1 crepe) – Calories 90, Total Fat 4.8 g, Saturated Fat 0.7 g, Cholesterol 39 mg, Sodium 24 mg, Carbohydrates 9 g, Fibre 1 g, Protein 3 g, Potassium 73 mg

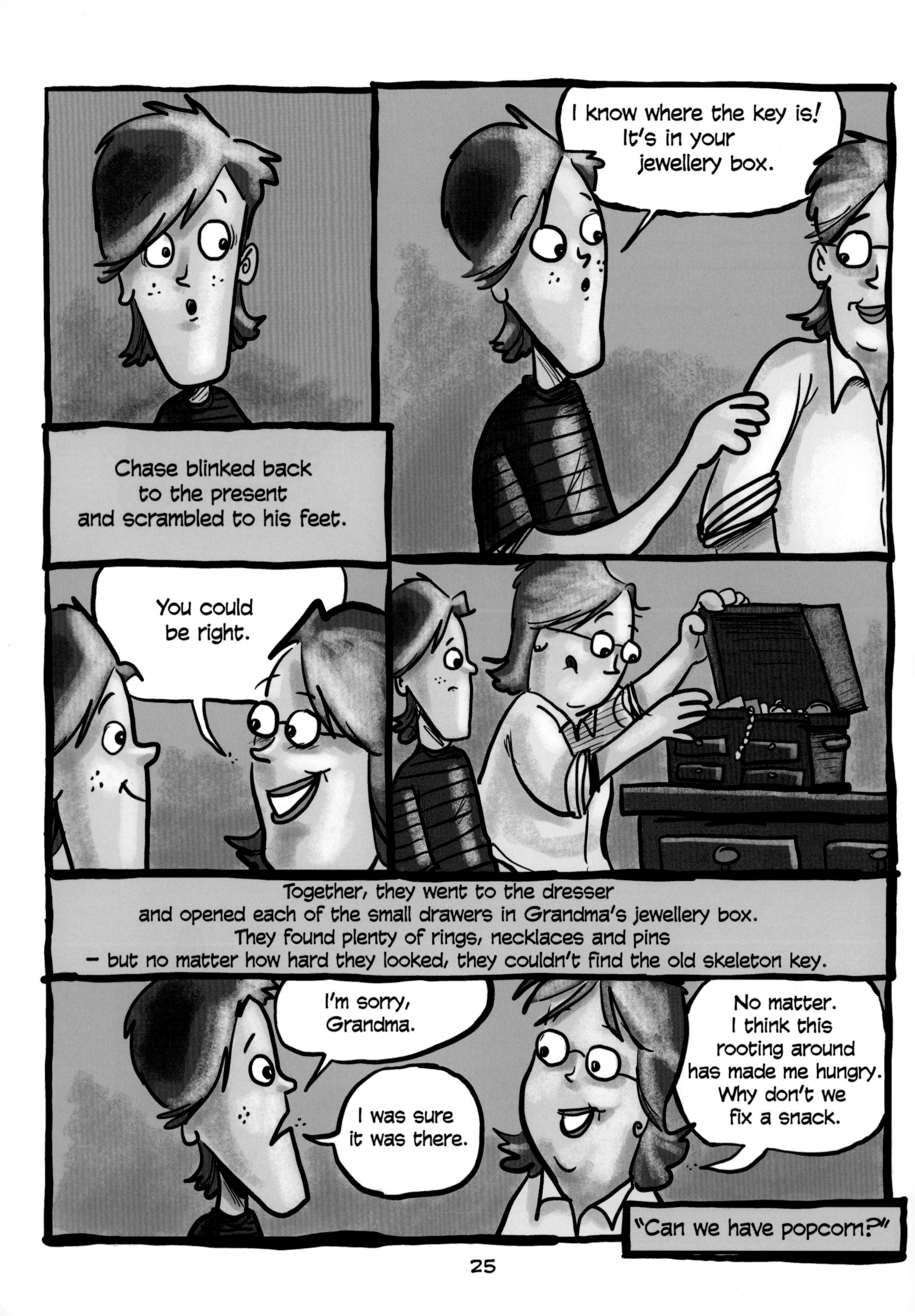
Chase blinked back
to the present
and scrambled to his feet.
I know where the key is!
It's in your
jewellery box.
You could
be right.
Together, they went to the dresser
and opened each of the small drawers in Grandma's jewellery box.
They found plenty of rings, necklaces and pins
– but no matter how hard they looked, they couldn't find the old skeleton key.
I'm sorry,
Grandma.
I was sure
it was there.
No matter.
I think this
rooting around
has made me hungry.
Why don't we
fix a snack.
"Can we have popcorn?"

We sure can!
"Why not grab that old cookbook. During the Great Depression, popcorn was a popular snack because people could afford it. My great, great grandmother, Ruth had all kinds of recipes for popcorn."
Even one with chocolate.
That's the one for me!
He flipped through the pages of the cookbook...
until he landed on the perfect recipe.
How about this one?
But when Chase looked up, he wasn't in his grandparent's house anymore.

The smell of popcorn overwhelmed Chase in the dimly lit theatre. Rows and rows of fancy, high-backed chairs faced a giant black movie screen.
Dozens of people filtered in through the doors and settled into their seats.
Chase sat alone behind a young couple holding hands, and sharing a bag of popcorn
What are we going to do about the drought? ... And the grasshoppers?.

The grasshoppers? Chase leaned forward to better hear the conversation.
That was quite something, wasn't it, Ruth?
The man threw a piece of popcorn into his mouth and bit down.
I've never seen grasshoppers so thick! They were like a dust storm rolling up the field.
Some of our neighbours are calling them "the black blizzard".
Chase caught the woman's profile and felt a tingle of familiarity. Who was she?
Don't worry, Ruth, we'll get through this. We still have plenty of bacon, right?

Chase remembered one of his grandmother's stories about the old days and how during the 1930s pork was one of the only meats available. Hundreds of families lost their farms due to several years of drought. People went hungry. It was a scary time in history.

The woman noticed the key just as
a black and white film flickered onto the screen:
The Count of Monte Cristo, one of Grandpa's favourite movies.

Middle Eastern Popcorn

Popcorn's a good snack that can be changed with different toppings. Use your imagination.

How Many: For you and 4 friends

What You Need:

3 Tbsp canola oil, 45 mL
½ cup popcorn kernels*, 125 mL
3 Tbsp canola oil, 45 mL
½ tsp paprika, 2 mL
¼ tsp freshly ground pepper, 1 mL
1 tsp cumin, 5 mL
1 tsp oregano, 5 mL
½ tsp garlic powder, 2 mL
¼ tsp dried red pepper flakes, 1 mL

***TIP:** ½ cup (125 mL) unpopped popcorn = 10 cups popped popcorn.

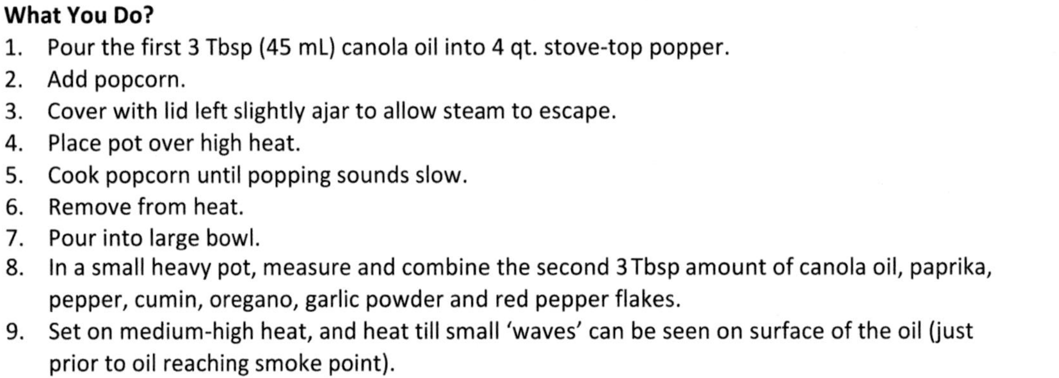

What You Do?

1. Pour the first 3 Tbsp (45 mL) canola oil into 4 qt. stove-top popper.
2. Add popcorn.
3. Cover with lid left slightly ajar to allow steam to escape.
4. Place pot over high heat.
5. Cook popcorn until popping sounds slow.
6. Remove from heat.
7. Pour into large bowl.
8. In a small heavy pot, measure and combine the second 3 Tbsp amount of canola oil, paprika, pepper, cumin, oregano, garlic powder and red pepper flakes.
9. Set on medium-high heat, and heat till small 'waves' can be seen on surface of the oil (just prior to oil reaching smoke point).
10. *Be careful not to burn yourself with the hot oil!* Drizzle over popcorn.
11. Toss popcorn to mix ingredients.

How healthy is it?

1 serving (2 cups of popcorn) – 201 Calories, Total Fat 17.5 g, Saturated Fat 1.3 g, Cholesterol 0 mg, Sodium 1.0 mg, Carbohydrates 12 g, Fibre 2.8 g, Protein 2 g, Potassium 12 mg

Berry Fruit-sicles

Great as a breakfast smoothie, but refreshing on a warm summer day!

How Many: For you and 3-5 friends, depending on the size of the ice-pop mold.

What You Need:

1 medium banana
½ cup blueberries, 125 mL
½ cup strawberries, 125 mL
½ cup green tea, cooled, 125 mL
½ cup cranberry juice, 125 mL
2 tsp canola oil, 10 mL

What You Do:

1. In the blender container, measure and add the banana, blueberries, strawberries, green tea, cranberry juice, and canola oil.
2. Blend ingredients until combined.
3. Pour the berry mixture into 4-6ice-pop molds or paper cups.
4. Place the cups or molds in the freezer for 2 – 3 hours. If using paper cups, check on the fruitsicles after 20 minutes. If they are starting to freeze, insert a wooden stick into the center of each fruitsicle and put them back in the freezer for the remaining time.
5. Once frozen, rinse the fruitsicle under warm water till the fruit leaves the side of the container. Remove the fruitsicle from the mold.
6. Enjoy.

How healthy is it?

1 serving (1/4 the recipe) – 120 Calories, Total Fat 2.5 g, Saturated Fat 0.2 g, Cholesterol 0 mg, Sodium 3 mg, Carbohydrates 16 g, Fibre 1.6 g, Protein 0.6 g, Potassium 152 mg

Onion Cakes

Traditional to Western Canadian ethnic restaurants, onion cakes have become a comfort food for many.

How Many: For you and 29 friends (30 cakes)

What You Need:

4 green onions, chopped
2½ cups whole wheat flour, 625 mL
2 cups all-purpose flour, 500 mL
1 tsp baking soda, 5 mL
2 cups water, 500 mL
2 tsp canola oil to mix with the dough, 10 mL
1 Tbsp canola oil, to brush lightly on both sides of the onion cakes, 15 mL

For Dipping:

Low-salt soy sauce, red wine vinegar, or mustard

What You Do:

1. Clean a counter top thoroughly, on which the dough will be able to be kneaded.
2. Wash green onions. Remove root end and any flimsy stems. Chop into 1 cm (½-inch) pieces. Set aside.
3. Measure and mix 4 cups (1 L) of the flour (2 cups barley and 2 cups all-purpose flour), in a large mixing bowl. Set aside the remaining 1⁄2 cup (125 mL) of flour to use later on if the dough gets sticky.
4. Measure and add to the flours, the baking soda and chopped green onion.
5. Measure and add 2 cups (500 mL) of water and 2 tsp (10 mL) of canola oil to the flour mixture. Mix together to make the dough.
6. Sprinkle some of the extra flour on the clean counter top.
7. Place the dough on the lightly floured surface and knead *(See How-To knead under Prairie Biscuits in the Breakfast Recipes)* for 5 minutes. If the dough becomes sticky, sprinkle some of the remaining flour over it.
8. Divide the dough evenly into 30 pieces.
9. Flatten the dough pieces with the palm of your hand on the lightly floured surface. Again, if the dough becomes sticky, sprinkle some flour over it.
10. Heat a non-stick frying pan on medium heat.
11. Lightly brush both sides of the onion cakes with a little canola oil, and then place them (about 6 at a time) in the hot pan and cook until golden brown, about 1 to 2 minutes on each side.
12. If you wish, serve the onion cakes with soy sauce, red vinegar or chili sauce to dip them in.

How healthy is it?

1 serving (1 onion cake, no dipping sauce) – 71 Calories, Total Fat 1.1 g, Saturated Fat 0.1 g, Cholesterol 0 mg, Sodium 42 mg, Carbohydrates 14 g, Fibre 1.3 g, Protein 2.2 g, Potassium 45 mg

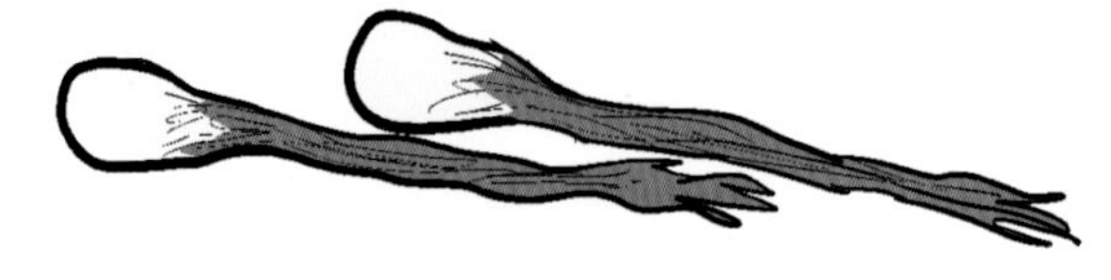

Monster Cookies

Sweet and special...Add more chocolate, change the nuts, or add some dried fruit like cherries and these will please even more of your family and friends.

How Many: For you and 35 friends (36 cookies) or as an after school snack for a whole month, OR 2 bases for cookie pizzas.

What You Need:

canola baking spray
½ cup canola oil, 125 mL
½ cup canola non-hydrogenated margarine, 125 mL
1 cup firmly packed brown sugar, 250 mL
1 cup granulated sugar, 250 mL
3 eggs
1 Tbsp vanilla extract, 15 mL
2½ cups all-purpose flour, 625 mL
½ tsp salt, 2 mL
2 tsp baking soda, 10 mL
1½ cups rolled oats, 375 mL
½ cup mini candy-coated chocolate pieces, 125 mL
½ cup chopped walnuts, optional, 125 mL

What You Do:

1. Preheat oven to 350°F (180°C).
2. Take out a baking sheet or pizza tin. Spray with canola baking spray.
3. In a small bowl, crack the eggs one at a time. Make sure not to get any eggshells in the eggs. Transfer the cracked eggs to a large mixing bowl.
4. Measure and add non-hydrogenated margarine, brown sugar, granulated sugar and vanilla to the eggs. Beat until light and fluffy.
5. In a separate bowl, measure and combine flour, salt and baking soda, then add to the egg mixture.
6. Measure and fold in the rolled oats, candy coated chocolate pieces, and walnuts.
7. Scoop and drop a spoonful of the cookie dough onto the baking sheet. Continue until all of the cookie dough has been used. Make sure to leave a little bit of space between each spoonful of cookie dough to allow the cookies to expand. If you are making a cookie pizza, then divide the dough in two, and form a 'large' cookie that covers the pizza tin.
8. Bake Monster cookies for 10 minutes in the preheated oven, and until cookies are golden brown on the edges. OR bake pizza cookie for 15 minutes or until golden brown.
9. Transfer cookies or pizza cookie to a wire rack to cool.
10. For the pizza cookie, cover the cookie with Greek yogurt, and top with a variety of fresh fruits and a few 50%+ cacao chocolate shavings.

How healthy is it?

1 serving (1 cookie) – 170 Calories, Total Fat 8.2 g, Saturated Fat 1.4 g, Cholesterol 16 mg, Sodium 131 mg, Carbohydrates 22 g, Fibre 0.9 g, Protein 2 g, Potassium 23 mg

1 serving (1/8 of one pizza base, fruit & yogurt not included) – 382 Calories, Total Fat 18.5 g, Saturated Fat 3.1 g, Cholesterol 35 mg, Sodium 294 mg, Carbohydrates 50 g, Fibre 2 g, Protein 5 g, Potassium 51 mg

Chase shook his head to clear the image. "Grandma, where do you keep your purses?"
She turned from the stove, where she had just made a huge pot of popcorn.
In my closet. Why?
Come on.
I think the key is in one of them!
But after going through each and every one of Grandma's handbags,
they could find no trace of the lost skeleton key.
It's okay Chase. Let's go have some popcorn and talk about this school bake-off.

In the excitement of the missing key, Chase had forgotten all about his mission to find a recipe great enough to win the school baking competition.
"Maybe there's something in that old cookbook," he said.
Family Recipes
"Let's take a look," Grandma said.
Maybe I'll make Grandpa some of those fancy lunchbox granola bars he likes so much.
Chase re-opened the cookbook. His skin prickled. He squeezed his eyes shut – and opened them to...
Family Recipes
You ain't Nothing but a hound dog!

What kind of
lyrics were those?
Chase covered his ears
and looked around the room.
The diner was full –
not even one seat
open for him.
The air was ripe with
the scent of hamburgers
and French fries. Milkshakes
of various flavours dotted
the tables, where groups of
teens chatted
over the sound of that
silly hound dog song.

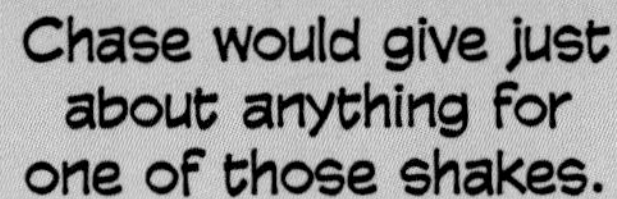
Chase would give just
about anything for
one of those shakes.

He was just about to ask, when the Elvis guy stopped singing, and another man headed to the microphone. He tapped the tip of the mike.
Testing testing
ROCK and
He definitely had everyone's attention.
I'm Peter Black and I'll be your auctioneer for today's Box Social.
Remember, ladies, you aren't allowed to tell the boys which is your lunch box.

He motioned to a table filled with decorated boxes. They reminded Chase of Chinese food containers, only each of them was covered with hand-drawn pictures or covered in various brightly-coloured fabrics.
nd ROLL
"If a fellow picks yours, he shares your meal with you."
Shall we get started?
A chorus of cheers filled the diner.

The auctioneer held up the first container and the bidding began.
Chase strained to make out the words, but the man spoke so fast, the scene became a whir of laughter and noise.
Teenage Grandma shifted in her seat.
From the corner of his eye he spotted a young woman sitting alone, her hands folded neatly in her lap.
Chase recognized his grandmother right away.
She couldn't have been more than fifteen years old.
The auctioneer took the next container to the podium.
Her eyes widened.

Bright yellow
canola-type flowers
covered the container
in the auctioneer's hand.
That had to be Grandma's.
Sure enough, Chase spotted
his grandfather
just as he secured
the winning bid
on Grandma's lunch box.

Teenage Grandpa let out a loud whistle and a cheer.

A few minutes later, Chase's teenaged grandparents found a spot at the back of the diner.
I hope you like it.
Grandma's voice was low and sweet. "I made your favourite."

Grandpa held the container up to his nose and sniffed. "Is that what I think it is?"

Chase leaned in...
but couldn't see inside.

"Wow-ee! I hope you've got this recipe under lock and key."

Grandma tapped the pocket on the front of her blouse and winked. "I'll never let the key out of my sight."

Lunchbox Granola Bars

Great for lunch, breakfast or snack!

How many: For you and 23 friends (24 bars), or wrapped in plastic and frozen, a school snack for a whole month.

What you need:

2 cups rolled oats, 500 mL
1 cup whole wheat flour, 250 mL
½ cup ground flaxseeds, 125 mL
⅓ cup packed brown sugar, 75 mL
1 tsp ground cinnamon, 5 mL
1 cup raisins, or your favorite dried fruit, 250 mL
½ cup unsalted sunflower seeds, 125 mL
¼ tsp salt, 1 mL
¼ cup canola oil, 60 mL
⅓ cup honey, 75 mL
1 egg
¼ cup unsweetened applesauce, 60 mL
2 tsp vanilla extract, 10 mL

What you do:

1. Preheat oven to 350°F (180°C).
2. Brush a light layer of canola oil on a 9 x 13 inch (22 x 33-cm) baking pan.
3. In large mixing bowl, measure oats, flour, flaxseed, brown sugar, cinnamon, raisins, sunflower seeds and salt.
4. Mix well.
5. Make a well in the center of the dry ingredients.
6. In a small bowl, crack the egg. Make sure to not get any eggshells in with the egg.
7. Using a fork, beat the egg till frothy. Add the egg to the well in the dry ingredients.
8. Measure and add the canola oil, honey, applesauce and vanilla to the egg.
9. Mix the wet and dry ingredients together.
10. Pat the mixture evenly into the baking pan.
11. Mark off the mixture into 24 bars.
12. Bake 20 to 25 minutes until the edges begin to turn golden brown.
12. Let the baking pan cool for 5 minutes, then cut into the bars while still warm. Do not allow the bars to cool completely before cutting, or they will be too hard to cut.

How healthy is it?

1 serving (1 bar) – Calories 141, Total Fat 6 g, Saturated Fat 0.6 g, Cholesterol 8 mg, Sodium 43 mg, Carbohydrates 20 g, Fibre 2 g, Protein 3 g, Potassium 25 mg

It's Cool Outside Soup

Comfort food for Canadian winters – or a cool, rainy summer day!

How much: 10 servings

What you need:

2 tsp canola oil, 10 mL
1 cup dry red lentils, 250 mL
¼ cup quick-cooking barley, 50 mL
5 cups no-salt beef, chicken or veggie broth, 1.25 L
1 lb. lean ground beef, chicken or soy protein, 454 g
1 tsp onion powder, 5 mL
2 tsp garlic powder, 10 mL
2 carrots, chopped
2 celery stalks, chopped
1 cup corn, canned or frozen, 250 mL
1 28 oz can crushed tomatoes, 396 mL
2 tsp cumin powder, optional, 10 mL
½ tsp pepper, 2 mL
1 bay leaf

What you do:

1. Place a large stock pot on stove set on high heat. Add canola oil.
2. Add lentils and barley and stir to release some of the flavour from the lentils.
3. Add beef broth.
4. Bring mixture to a boil, reduce heat and simmer covered for 30 minutes.
5. In a non-stick skillet set at medium-high heat, sauté meat with onion and garlic powders.
6. Break up ground meat with spoon until there is no pink colour, about five minutes.
7. Add the meat to the stockpot.
8. Add the carrots, celery, corn, tomatoes, pepper and bay leaf. Also add cumin if you choose to use.
9. Bring the mixture to a boil. Reduce heat and simmer covered 20 to 30 minutes, or until Vegetables are tender. Stir occasionally.
10. Remove bay leaf.
11. Serve.

How healthy is it?

1 serving (1 cup) – Calories 201, Total Fat 4 g, Saturated Fat 0.7 g, Cholesterol 24 mg, Sodium 288 mg, Carbohydrates 25 g, Fibre 6 g, Protein 18 g, Potassium 533 mg

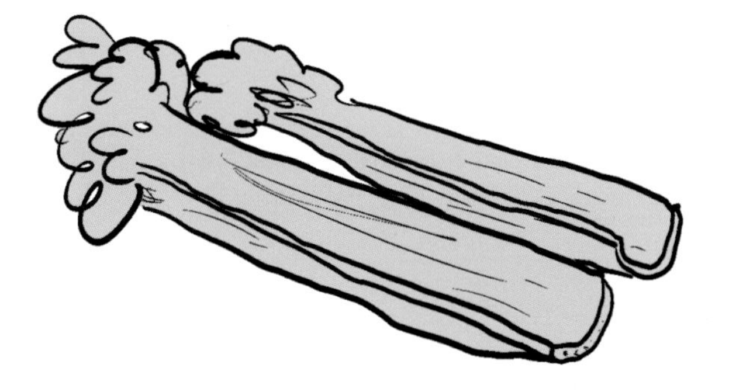

Macaroni & Cheese Muffins

Great travelling lunch version of an old favourite!

How Much: 24 muffins

What You Need:

2 cups uncooked whole wheat elbow macaroni, 500 mL
½ cup seasoned dry bread or whole wheat cracker crumbs, 125 mL
2 tsp canola oil, 10 mL
1 Tbsp non-hydrogenated canola margarine, 15 mL
1 egg
1 cup low-fat milk, 250 mL OR
1 cup low-salt tomato sauce, 250 mL
1 ½ cups lower-fat sharp Cheddar cheese, 375 mL
1 ½ cups lower-fat Mozzarella cheese, 375 mL
½ cup seasoned dry bread crumbs

What You Do:

1. Pre-heat oven to 350ºF (175ºC).
2. Grease a muffin tin with non-stick canola cooking spray.
3. Fill a large pot with water. Add a cover and set over high heat. Bring the water to boil.
4. In a small bowl, stir together the bread or cracker crumbs, and canola oil; set aside.
5. Add the macaroni to the boiling water - making sure not to burn yourself.
6. Cook the macaroni for about 8 minutes, or till the macaroni is still a little bit firm.
7. Remove the macaroni from the heat.
8. Pour into a colander to drain.
9. Return to the macaroni to the pan.
10. Measure and stir in the margarine and egg until pasta is evenly coated.
11. Reserve ½ cup (125 mL) of the sharp Cheddar cheese and stir the remaining Cheddar cheese, milk or tomato sauce, and mozzarella cheese into the pasta.
12. Spoon macaroni mixture into the prepared muffin tin.
13. Sprinkle the reserved cheese and the bread crumb mixture over the tops.
14. Bake for 30 minutes in the preheated oven, or until the topping is nicely browned.
15. Allow the muffins to cool for a few minutes before removing from the pan. This will allow the cheese to set and they will hold their muffin shape.

How healthy is it?

1 serving (2 muffins made with milk) – Calories 187, Total Fat 6 g, Saturated Fat 2.5 g, Cholesterol 27 mg, Sodium 391 mg, Carbohydrates 22 g, Fibre 2 g, Protein 13 g, Potassium 83 mg

1 serving (2 muffins made with tomato sauce) – Calories 187, Total Fat 6 g, Saturated Fat 2.4 g, Cholesterol 26 mg, Sodium 385 mg, Carbohydrates 22 g, Fibre 2 g, Protein 12 g, Potassium 53 mg

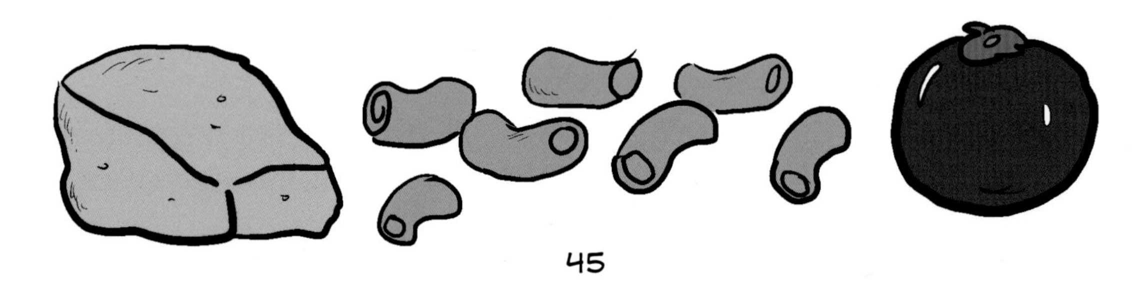

P.S. I love You Salad

So tasty, with so much variety it's difficult for anyone to say this is not a favourite.

How Much: For you and 8 friends (9-1 cup [250 mL] salads)

What You Need:

Salad:

1 5-oz bag of mixed greens, 142g
2½ cups of fruit*, 625 mL
¼ cup toasted walnuts, coarsely chopped, 60 mL
*Choose 1 apple, 1 orange, 1 grapefruit, ½ cup (125 mL) strawberry slices, raspberries, Saskatoons, etc.

Juice Dressing:

2 Tbsp juice*, 30 mL
2 Tbsp canola oil, 30 mL
1 tsp vinegar, 5 mL
*Choose apple, orange, cranberry, strawberry, etc. juice.

Topping:

½ cup 50% or more cocoa chocolate shavings, 125 mL

What You Do:

1. Place washed mixed greens in a large salad bowl.
2. Choose fruit. Peel orange and pink grapefruit; cut into segments and add to the salad bowl. Rinse apple and chop. Rinse strawberries, raspberries and Saskatoons and add to the salad bowl.
3. Chop the walnuts and add to the salad bowl.
4. In a small bowl, measure and whisk together your favourite juice, canola oil and vinegar. This will be the dressing.
5. Right before serving the salad, pour the dressing over the salad and toss lightly.
6. Sprinkle dark chocolate shavings on top of the salad or over each individual salad plate.
7. Serve right away, as this salad is best when it is fresh.

How healthy is it?

1 serving– 115 Calories, Total Fat 8 g, Saturated Fat 2.3 g, Cholesterol 0 mg, Sodium 14 mg, Carbohydrates 12 g, Fibre 2.1 g, Protein 1.1 g, Potassium 68 mg
*used apple juice for the dressing

Chase blinked.
Of course. Grandma's closet!
I know where the key is!
Grandma had turned on some music, and a familiar Elvis Presley song belted through the radio. She was dancing around the kitchen, using her wooden spoon as a microphone.
"Oh dear. I fear I've sent you on quite the wild goose chase."
"Where do you keep your shirts? You know, your old ones?"
In the spare bedroom. But I don't know what you think you'll find there except for a few dust bunnies.
Chase rummaged through all of Grandma's old clothes. He reached into every pocket, but the old skeleton key wasn't there.

It's okay, Chase.
I'm sure it will turn up.
I'm not giving up.
family Recipes

Chase ran back to the kitchen and lifted the old cookbook.
He took a deep breath, and opened to a middle page. Mayonnaise.
The ingredient listing lifted off the page and swirled around him like Jupiter's moons.
Vegetable oil, honey, eggs... The words grew bigger and bigger and bigger until...
family

BOOM
A small explosion echoed in the lab and sparks sizzled from the bottom of a glass beaker. Test tubes, and other containers of various sizes bubbled and gurgled with unidentified liquids. Smoke billowed from miniature plates that were red with heat. A young woman in a lab coat was busily mopping up something white that had overflowed onto the bench.
I don't understand.
Chase thought at first she was speaking to him, but a quick glance around told him she had no idea Chase was in the room.
I followed all of the directions.
She adjusted her glasses and looked up towards Chase, almost through him.
"Grandma?"

She had to be 20 or something, maybe from her University days. Chase's grandmother leaned over her work bench and flipped over the page in the now-familiar *Family Cookbook*.
Eggs. Honey...
BOOM
Another mini explosion rocked the lab.
Oh shoot.
I'll never get this right.
Yes you will, Grandma. Keep trying!

But Chase's grandmother couldn't hear his words of encouragement.
She had no way of knowing that when she grew up,
she would become
a well-respected chemist.
Grandma poured some dry powder into a glass beaker.
Then added some liquid and set it on the hot plate.
The mixture bubbled and popped.
Whoa. Grandma's cooking had come a long way.

The lab door opened and a man that looked like a professor entered the room. He peered over Grandma's shoulder and made quiet tsk tsking sounds.
Let's call it a day, Joy.
I'll try again tomorrow.
Make sure you clean up this mess.
Joy tidied up the containers, emptied the glassware, and closed the book. She shoved it into her backpack, and after a pause, opened an empty can of baking soda and dropped the old skeleton key inside.
She glanced once more at her lab, and with a wink, disappeared into the shadows.

Porcupine Sliders

When Canadians started eating rice regularly, it was an ingredient in many dishes-including meat patties.

How Many: 1 for you and 11 friends (12 sliders)

What You Need:

canola baking spray
⅓ cup brown or wild rice rice, uncooked, 75 mL
¾ cup spinach leaves, 175 mL
1½ Tbsp dried cranberries, optional, 22.5 mL
1 tsp onion powder, 5 mL
2 tsp garlic powder, 10 mL
1 lb. ground turkey or chicken, extra lean, 454g
1 large egg
¾ tsp Worcestershire sauce, 3.75 mL
½ tsp black pepper, 2.5 mL
small whole-wheat dinner rolls

What You Do:

1. Preheat oven to 350°F (180°C).
2. Coat a baking sheet with canola baking spray. Set aside.
3. Cook rice according to package directions, excluding the salt in the cooking water. When done, drain well and spread on the baking sheet to cool completely.
4. Chop the spinach into shreds. Measure ½ cup (175 mL).
5. Chop cranberries into small pieces.
6. In a large mixing bowl, crack the egg. Make sure there are no eggshells in the egg. Using a fork, beat the egg till frothy.
7. Measure and add turkey, cranberries, spinach, onion and garlic powders, Worcestershire sauce, and black pepper to the egg. Mix well.
8. Add the cooled rice to the turkey mixture.
9. Mix well.
10. Using clean hands, form the mixture into 12 patties. Place on the baking sheet.
11. Wash your hands well.
12. Bake patties in the preheated oven for 20 to 25 minutes or until turkey reaches an internal temperature of 165ºF (74ºC).
13. Serve on whole-wheat rolls with mustard, optional canola mayonnaise, lettuce, tomato, and red onion.

How healthy is it?

1 serving, 1 slider – 68 Calories, Total Fat 1 g, Saturated Fat 0.1 g, Cholesterol 31 mg, Sodium 35 mg, Carbohydrates 5 g, Fibre 0.5 g, Protein 10.7 g, Potassium 37 mg

*analysis done with wild rice, cranberries & ground turkey. Dinner rolls not included in analysis

Chicken Fingers

Not the fast-food restaurant type, but healthier and easy to make.

How Many: Enough for you and 7 friends (8 chicken breasts)

What you need:

- canola baking spray
- 1½ cups fine whole-wheat bread crumbs, 375 mL
- ½ cup whole-wheat flour, 125 mL
- 1 tsp paprika, 5 mL
- 1 tsp basil or oregano, 5 mL
- 3 Tbsp canola oil, 45 mL
- 8 boneless, skinless chicken breasts halves

What You Do:

1. Preheat oven to 350 °F (180 °C).
2. Lightly oil a 9 x 13 inch (22 x 33 cm) baking dish with canola oil or spray with canola baking spray.
3. In a large bowl, measure and combine bread crumbs, flour, paprika and rosemary.
4. Measure and add the canola oil to the crumbs, mixing until well combined.
5. Slice chicken breast in half crosswise, then cut into 1/2-inch (1.25 cm) slices and finally into 1/2-inch (1.25 cm) strips (to resemble fries).
6. Roll each chicken breast strip in the breadcrumb mixture until the outside is coated. Place in the prepared baking dish.
7. Wash your hands with soap and water.
8. Clean the cutting board with a solution of bleach (1 tsp [5 mL] per gallon [4L] water), so that it doesn't contaminate other foods.
9. Throw away any crumb mixture that is left over.
10. Bake the chicken for 30 to 35 minutes in the preheated oven or until chicken is no longer pink in the middle and the juices run clear.

How healthy is it?

1 serving 1 chicken breast – 267 Calories, Total Fat 8.9 g, Saturated Fat 1.3 g, Cholesterol 73 mg, Sodium 81 mg, Carbohydrates 16 g, Fibre 2.4 g, Protein 30 g, Potassium 249 mg

Super-Duper Sweet Potato Salad

A tasty change for your next picnic.

How Much: For you and 4 friends (5 small salads)

What You Need:

3 large sweet potatoes (peeled and quartered)
3 Tbsp red wine vinegar, 45 mL
2 Tbsp orange juice, 30 mL
2 Tbsp maple syrup or honey, 30 mL
½ tsp mustard, 2.5 mL
black pepper (freshly ground, a few grinds!)
½ tsp cinnamon, 2.5 mL
2 Tbsp canola oil, 30 mL
1 large Granny Smith apple
½ cup dried cherries or cranberries, 125 mL
¼ cup unsalted sunflower seeds, optional 60 mL

What You Do:

1. Peel and quarter sweet potatoes. Place in a large saucepan. Add just enough water to cover the tops of the sweet potatoes. Cover the saucepan and bring the water to a boil over high heat.
2. Once the water is boiling, reduce the heat to medium-high and cook the sweet potatoes at a low boil. Cook until tender, so you can easily poke them with a fork, about 10 minutes.
3. Drain the sweet potatoes and transfer to a large bowl to cool.
4. In a small bowl, measure and whisk together the vinegar, orange juice, maple syrup or honey, mustard, pepper, and cinnamon.
5. Measure and add the canola oil to the vinegar mixture. Mix well and set aside.
6. Wash the apple, remove the core, cut into cubes and add to the sweet potatoes.
7. Measure and add the dried cherries to the potato mixture.
8. Add sunflower seeds to the mixture.
9. Gently toss the sweet potato salad with the dressing and serve warm or chilled.

How healthy is it?

1 serving – 258 Calories, Total Fat 9.6 g, Saturated Fat 8.9 g, Cholesterol 0 mg, Sodium 61 mg, Carbohydrates 40 g, Fibre 7.4 g, Protein 3.4 g, Potassium 285 mg
*analyzed with sunflower seeds and dried cherries

Bannock Pizza

Bannock is traditional to North America's indigenous people. Why not make it part of your family's recipe collection – but with an Italian twist by making it into pizza...

How Much: Enough for you and 5 friends (6 servings)

What You Need:

- 3 cups all-purpose flour with added fibre, 750 mL
- 3 cups whole-wheat flour, 750 mL
- 3 Tbsp baking powder, 45 mL
- ½ tsp salt, 2 mL
- ½ cup canola oil, 125 mL
- 3 cups lukewarm water, 750 mL
- canola baking spray
- 1¼ cups lower-salt tomato sauce, 300 mL
- 4 cups total sliced mushrooms, peppers, purple onion bits, artichokes, etc. 1L
- 1 cup lower-fat shredded mozzarella cheese, 250 mL

What You Do:

1. Preheat oven to 400°F (200°C).
2. In a large mixing bowl, measure and mix flours, baking powder and salt.
3. Make a well in the centre, add canola oil and approximately two-thirds of the water. Stir using a fork. Add more water, if necessary, so that the mixture forms a stiff dough.
4. Shape dough into a ball. Knead *(See How-To knead under Prairie Biscuits in Breakfast Recipes)* lightly, 8 to 10 times.
5. Divide dough into two portions (for two pizzas) or into 16 portions (for individual appetizer pizzas). Pat/press each portion into a flat circle approximately 1-inch (2.5 cm) thick.
6. Pour 1 Tbsp (15 mL) canola oil in frying pan, set on medium-low heat.
7. Add the bannock dough and cook for 10 minutes per side or until golden brown on each side.
8. Cool the bannock.
9. Top each bannock piece with tomato sauce, your favourite toppings and shredded cheese. Bake until cheese starts to bubble.
10. Cut into slices and serve.

How healthy is it?

1 serving of bannock – 612 Calories, Total Fat 21 g, Saturated Fat 1.7 g, Cholesterol 0 mg, Sodium 1026 mg, Carbohydrates 95 g, Fibre 8.1 g, Protein 14 g, Potassium 285 mg

1 serving of bannock pizza – 710 Calories, Total Fat 24 g, Saturated Fat 3.4 g, Cholesterol 10 mg, Sodium 1168 mg, Carbohydrates 107 g, Fibre 10 g, Protein 22 g, Potassium 680 mg

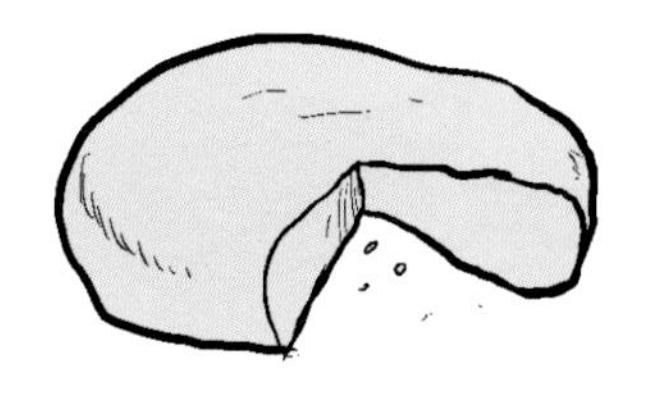

Fairy Tale Fries

Finger foods are always fun to eat – and they can be healthy too!

How much: 6 servings ½ cup (125 mL) fries + 2 Tbsp (30 mL) sauce

What you need:

Fries:

1½ lbsweet potatoes, Yukon Gold potatoes, carrots, or parsnips, 750 g
2 Tbsp canola oil, 30 mL
1 tsp paprika, 5 mL
½ tsp coarsely ground black pepper, 2 mL

Cajun Aioli Dipping Sauce:

1 Tbsp pasteurized egg yolk, 15 mL
½ Tbsp vinegar, 7.5 mL
½ Tbsp water, 7.5 mL
½ tsp mustard, 2.5 mL
¾ cup canola oil, 175 mL
¼ tsp pepper, 1.25 mL
1 tsp lemon juice, 5 mL

¾ cup no-fat sour cream, optional, 175 mL
½-1 Tbsp hot sauce, optional, 7.5-15 mL

What you do:

1. Preheat oven to 450°F (230°C).
2. Line large baking sheet with aluminum foil or parchment paper.
3. Place vegetables in large bowl.
4. Drizzle canola oil over vegetables and toss gently, yet thoroughly to coat.
5. Sprinkle with paprika and black pepper and toss gently.
6. Arrange veggies in single layer on baking sheet.
7. Bake carrots or parsnips for 15 to 20 minutes; potatoes or sweet potatoes for 30 to 35 minutes. Stir after 10 to 15 minutes or when beginining to brown.
8. Serve immediately for peak flavor and texture.

While the veggies are baking, make the aioli (another name for mayonnaise).

1. Measure the egg yolk, vinegar, water and mustard, and add to a blender container.
2. Place the lid on the blender container, and blend until the mixture is slightly foamy.
3. Measure the canola oil.
4. Remove the centre portion of the lid for the blender container.
5. Turn the blender on slow.
6. With the motor running, slowly drizzle the canola oil into the blender through the lid hole. Note how the mixture starts thickening.
7. Add pepper and lemon juice.

NOTE: To reduce the calories in the sauce, mix the aioli with the sour cream. Season with the hot sauce.

How healthy is it?

1 serving (½ cup [125 mL] sweet potatoes) – Calories 74, Total Fat 5 g, Saturated Fat 0.4 g, Cholesterol 0 mg, Sodium 39 mg, Carbohydrates 15 g, Fibre 3 g, Protein 2 g, Potassium 239 mg

1 serving (½ cup [125 mL] potatoes) – Calories 119, Total Fat 5 g, Saturated Fat 0.4 g, Cholesterol 0 mg, Sodium 5 mg, Carbohydrates 18 g, Fibre 2 g, Protein 2 g, Potassium 311 mg

1 serving (½ cup [125 mL] carrots) – Calories 77, Total Fat 5 g, Saturated Fat 0.4 g, Cholesterol 0 mg, Sodium 46 mg, Carbohydrates 8 g, Fibre 3 g, Protein 1 g, Potassium 220 mg

1 serving (½ cup [125 mL] parsnips) – Calories 101, Total Fat 5 g, Saturated Fat 0.4 g, Cholesterol 0 mg, Sodium 9 mg, Carbohydrates 14 g, Fibre 4 g, Protein 1 g, Potassium 265 mg

1 serving (2 Tbsp[30 mL] aioli) – Calories 257, Total Fat 29 g, Saturated Fat 2.3 g, Cholesterol 28 mg, Sodium 1 mg, Carbohydrates 0 g, Fibre 0 g, Protein 1 g, Potassium 5 mg

1 serving (2 Tbsp[30 mL] aioli/non-fat sour cream) –Calories 141, Total Fat 14 g, Saturated Fat 1.2 g, Cholesterol 16 mg, Sodium 26 mg, Carbohydrates 2 g, Fibre 0 g, Protein 1 g, Potassium 3 mg

The pantry!
Chase washed down a Lunchbox Granola Square with a glass of water.
Oh dear, not again.
"I got it, Grandma!"
I know where the key is. It's in your baking soda box.
I go through a box of baking soda regularly.
I would know if it was there.
What about old tins? I know you keep some.
Let's take a look.

Chase opened each and every old tin. He found leftover rice, a 1964 penny, and a few bugs. But the skeleton key was nowhere to be found.

But with every dead end, Chase began to wonder if the key wasn't lost for good.

"Come on, let's make grandpa a treat."

Family Recipes

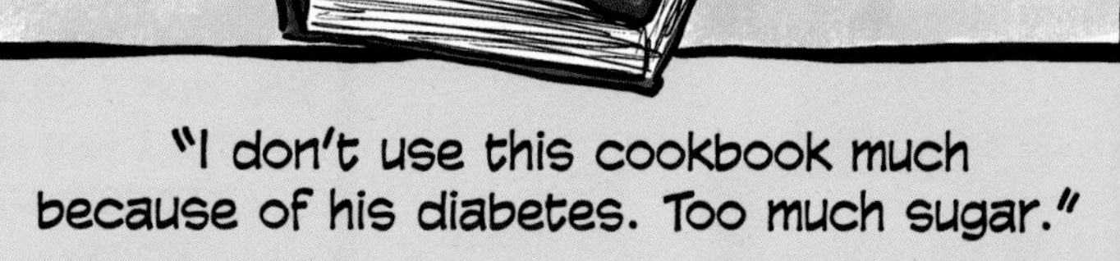

Chase knew too much sugar wasn't good for anyone. Coach Taylor always said the best energy came from whole foods, vegetables, grains, proteins and good fats, like canola oil.

"I still remember the day your Grandpa came back from the doctor's office," Grandma said, as she wiped a tear from the corner of her eye. "We made a lot of changes after that. The year was 2001..."

Grandma and Grandpa sat at the kitchen table, leafing through medical brochures and information pamphlets. Chase's Mom and Dad were across from his grandparents, looking worried.
"How can we help?"
"We need to learn about healthy cooking," Grandma said. "All of us."
So, no more sweets?
You don't have to give them up altogether, honey.
A small piece of birthday cake or pumpkin pie can still be planned for special occasions.

Some of the recipes in here sound delicious.
Healthy Eating
Sure, if you're a rabbit.
We'll get through this, dear.
Chase's Mom tapped the cover of the old family cookbook.
I guess we can put this away for awhile.
Healthy Eating
Family Recipes
But what about the...?
Now, let me go put this somewhere safe.
Grandma pressed her fingers to her lips.
"Don't worry, dear.
I've got that under lock and key."

Chase followed his grandmother into the bedroom.

She tucked the key into her jewellery box.

Chase frowned.
They'd checked there, first thing.
The key wasn't there.
So where did it go?
He heard soft footsteps behind him.

Grandpa?
Chase's grandfather closed the bedroom door behind him and crept to the jewellery box. He quietly opened the drawer, removed the key and walked to his dresser.
Chase watched in awe as his grandfather buried the key at the bottom of his sock drawer.
Now it all made sense.

As the vision faded, Chase grabbed his grandmother's hand once again and tugged her toward the bedroom.
I'm positive this time. I know where the key is.
Grandma chuckled. "Chase, darling, we've checked my jewellery cabinet. My closet. My shirt pockets and purses. It's simply not there."
I know it sounds crazy, Grandma. But trust me!

At Grandpa's dresser, Chase slowly opened the bottom drawer. He reached inside and rummaged through the socks...
... until he felt the cold metal of the key against his skin.
He held it up for Grandma.
I don't believe it!
Grandpa hid it.
But why?
Why that little sneak.
She went over to the bed and reached for the old tin box, inserted the key into the lock and turned the handle.
The box opened.
What's so special about what's in the box?

Grandma took out a small, rectangular recipe card and thrust it toward Chase.
This! Your grandfather's favourite cookies.
MONSTER COOKIES!
Chase suddenly knew exactly what recipe he was going to make for the bake-off.
Grandma, can you help me make these? Right now?

An hour and a half later, covered in flour, Chase took his first batch of cookies out of the oven. Their sweet smell made his stomach rumble with hunger.
Not until after dinner!
Minutes later, Grandpa came in from the field, hot and sweaty. He stepped into the kitchen and took a deep breath.
Joy? Are those...?
Yes dear, your favourite.
Chase made them.
Well, I'll be.
Grandpa stole a cookie right from the pan.
He bit in. Chewed. Swallowed.
These are delicious! Almost as good as Grandma's.
Chase only needed them to be better than Lightening's cinnamon buns and Nikolai's fudge brownies.

Chase, Lightening and Nikolai stood at the front of the class waiting for Mr. Lawrence to finish tasting Chase's monster cookie pizza.

Chase's heart pounded so fast he could hardly hold it in.

Lightening's cinnamon buns dripped with icing, and even Chase thought Nikolai's fudge brownies looked gooey and delicious.

But Mr. Lawrence made loud noises with every bite of Chase's cookie pizza, and he kept licking his chocolate and yogurt-covered lips.

I am impressed boys.
There is something special about each of your entries.
Chase held his breath.
But of course, there can only be one winner.
The winner of this year's bake-off is...
1ST

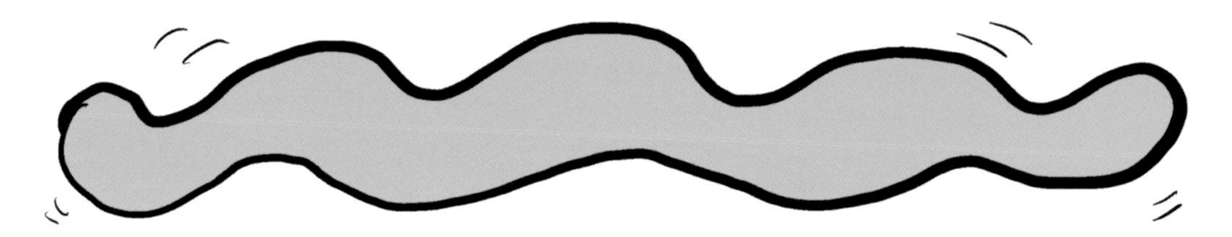

Gifts from the Kitchen

Electro-Active Slime

Why Electro-Active? Take a small piece of polystyrene foam (e.g., Styrofoam) and rub it on dry hair or a cat. Place near the slime and watch the material edge toward the foam or even break off and stick to it.

What You Need:

¾ cup cornstarch. 175 mL
2 cups canola oil, 500 mL
few drops of food colouring

What You Do:

1. Mix the cornstarch and canola oil together.
2. Add a few drops of food colouring of your choice.
3. Refrigerate the slime.
4. Separation of the ingredients is normal, so when you are ready to play with the slime, stir the ingredients together. Have fun!
5. The slime will be thick when it has just come from the refrigerator, but will flow more readily as it warms up. You can use temperature to control the consistency of the slime or you can add a bit more cornstarch for thicker slime or a small amount of additional canola oil for thinner electro-active slime.

How to Store:

You can store the slime in a sealed container, such as a bowl or a plastic bag. The slime is good for a couple of days at room temperature or at least a week if stored in the refrigerator.

Spiced Lemon Foot Soak

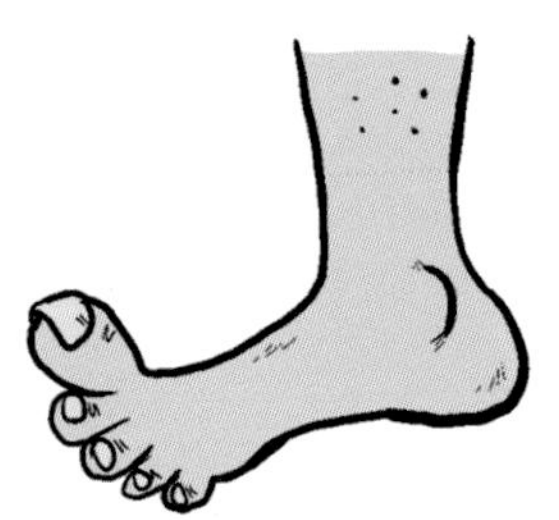

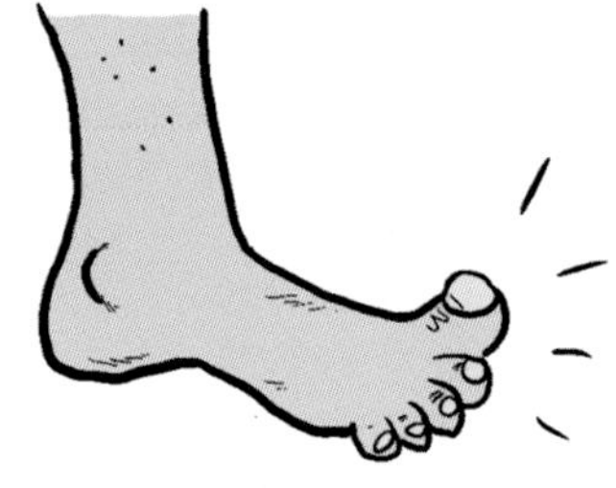

Great as a foot soak...wonderful for the entire body!

What You Need:

- 1 cup lemon juice, 250 mL
- ¼ tsp ground cinnamon, 1 mL
- ¼ tsp ground cloves, 1 mL
- 2 Tbsp canola oil, 30 mL
- ¼ cup milk, 50 mL

What You Do:

1. In the jar of the blender, measure all the ingredients.
2. Blend on medium speed till well mixed.
3. Store in glass container in refrigerator.
4. To use, add a couple of tablespoons (30-45 mL) to a small foot soaking tub or to a full bath. Soak, rinse with clear water and mild soap.

Fruity Play Dough

Make several batches so that your sculptures can boast a variety of colours.

What You Need:

2¼ cups all-purpose flour, 550 mL
1 cup salt, 250 mL
2 Tbsp unsweetened powder drink mix, 30 mL
4 Tbsp canola oil, 60 mL
¾-1 cup water, 175-250 mL

What You Do:

1. In a large bowl, measure flour, salt and powdered drink mix. Mix well.
2. Make a well in the centre of the flour mixture.
3. Measure the canola oil and ¾ cup (175 mL) water.
4. Stir until the mixture is the consistency of bread dough. If it's too dry, add more water a tablespoon (15 mL) at a time.
5. Spread a small amount of flour on a clean counter surface.
6. Place dough on the flour, and knead for 2-3 minutes or until the dough is firm and smooth.
7. Start sculpting!
8. Store dough in an airtight container or plastic bag, in the refrigerator till the dough is required again.

Milk Bones for My Pal Rex

Thanks to "In the Dog Kitchen" by J. Van Rosendaal from which this recipe was adapted.

How Many: about 36 'bones' depending on size of bone

What You Need:

2 cups whole wheat flour, 500 mL
½ cup wheat germ, 125 mL
¼ cup skim milk powder, 50 mL
pinch of salt
½ cup no-salt chicken stock or water, 125 mL
¼ cup canola oil, 50 mL
1 Tbsp molasses or honey, 15 mL
1 egg

What You Do:

1. Preheat oven to 350°F (180°C).
2. In a large bowl, measure and combine the flour, wheat germ, skim milk powder, and salt.
3. In a small bowl, stir together stock or water, canola oil, molasses or honey, and egg.
4. Add the liquid ingredients to the dry ingredients and stir until well blended.
5. Spread a small amount of flour on a clean counter.
6. Turn dough onto the floured surface. Knead *(see How-To in Pioneer Biscuits)* the dough a couple of times.
7. Using a rolling pin, roll out dough ¼-½ inch (0.5-1 cm) thick.
8. Cut the dough into bone shapes with a cookie cutter or knife.
9. Transfer cookie shapes to an ungreased cookie sheet.
10. Using a fork, prick each cookie several times.
11. Bake for 20 minutes, depending on the size and thickness of the cookies, until pale golden and firm.
12. Turn the oven off, but leave the 'bones' inside for a few hours to harden as they cool.
13. Store in a tightly sealed container.

Other 'Gift from the Kitchen' recipes available –

- *Recipes for Kids & the Toy Oven that Bakes*
- *Better Baking Mixes*
- *Sweet Dessert Mixes*
- *Other spa, pet treats, etc. available from www.learncanola.com*

Creating a Family Cookbook

A wonderful gift for family and friends, a family cookbook combines the treasured family recipes, with the memories of special moments and the people who created them.

TO CREATE A FAMILY COOKBOOK:

I. Develop a sample recipe format that you can ask everyone to follow. Be sure to include:

a. Name of the recipe
b. Name of the person contributing the recipe
c. Name of the person who originated the recipe (if different from the one submitting)
d. The history of the recipe (Where did it come from and why is it special?)
e. Ingredients and quantities needed, in the order in which they appear in the directions
f. Preparation and cooking directions
g. Optional or alternative ingredient choices – e.g. rhubarb rather than cherries
h. Cooking time
i. The number of people the recipe serves
j. Any special cooking tips or advice

II. Collect the Recipes

a. Send recipe request and sample recipe format sheet to your relatives
b. Request that recipes be received by a specified date
c. Encourage recipes that have been passed down through generations, as well as stories/photos of cooking with that person
d. If there's a family member that cooks by instinct, try to recruit someone else to go cooking with them so that they can write down the recipe, the techniques and how much "a pinch" truly is
e. Ask if those who submit recipes would like to receive a copy of the book

III. Organize the Cookbook

a. by category - appetizers, soups, salads, entrees and desserts
b. by individuals - grandparents, cousins, etc.
c. by family - by family unit (Mom, Dad & kids) or branch of the family tree (Grandma, Grandpa and all of their descendants)
d. by holiday - Christmas, Birthdays, Thanksgiving, etc.

IV. Assemble the Cookbook

a. Decide on a theme – family picture reunion, family crest, etc.
b. Photocopy the recipe submissions or re-type and format all you've received
c. Create a table of contents and an index
d. Write an introduction – why was this project done, when, and the reaction of family members
e. Include family history, photos, stories on how a recipe was discovered as fillers for pages, when a recipe does not need an entire page.
f. Decide to photocopy and use three-ring binders to hold the recipes, or to hire the services of a professional printer.

V. Distribute the Family Cookbook

a. Pat yourself on the back for a great job keeping family history and culinary traditions alive!

MY GREAT, GREAT GRANDMOTHER/FATHER
Josephine / Ernie

RECIPE:
Biscuits

MY GREAT GRANDMOTHER/FATHER
Ruth / Arthur

RECIPE:
Popcorn

MY GRANDMOTHER/FATHER
Joy / William

RECIPE:
Granola Bars

MY MOTHER/FATHER
Judy / Len

RECIPE:
Porcupine Sliders

MY SISTER
Amelia Duffy

RECIPE:
PlayDough

ME
Chase Superman Duffy

RECIPE:
Monster Cookie Pizza

CHASE SUPERMAN DUFFY RECIPE FAMILY TREE